For my wonderful Mam and Dad, with love – J G

To Daniel – T W

This edition published by Scholastic Inc.,
557 Broadway, New York, NY 10012,
by arrangement with Little Tiger Press.
Scholastic and associated logos
are trademarks and/or registered
trademarks of Scholastic Inc.
Scholastic Canada Ltd.: Markham, Ontario

First published in the United States by Good Books,
Intercourse, PA 17534, 2010

Original edition published in English by Little Tiger Press,
an imprint of Magi Publications, London, England, 2010

Text copyright © Magi Publications 2010
Illustrations copyright © Tim Warnes 2010

ISBN: 978-1-84895-154-9

Printed in Heshan, China

2 4 6 8 10 9 7 5 3

Silent Night

Juliet Groom   Tim Warnes

All the animals gather together,

Silent, harmonious, and happy forever.

Sleep in heavenly peace,
All together in peace.

Silent night, holy night,
Lift your hearts in joy tonight.

Take joy in our world, in the mountains so tall,
The flowers, so tiny — take joy in them all.

Celebrate all that we share,
Each precious moment we share.

Silent night, holy night,
Angels sing of love's pure light.

Love that brings a smile to each face,
That brightens each day with its
beauty and grace.

Cherish those dear to your heart,
Keep them safe, safe in your heart.

Silent night, holy night,
All the world holds its breath tonight.

High above, a bright star gleams,

A child is born, and heaven's gift brings

. . . Hope for all in the world,

Hope for our beautiful world.